CORONAVIRUS
is BOO BOO

Written and illustrated by

Dr. Cate Le

LCCN: 2020921748
ISBN: 978-1-7360641-0-8 (Hardcover)
ISBN: 978-1-7360641-2-2 (Paperback)
ISBN: 978-1-7360641-1-5 (ePub)

For information, contact:
Catherine Le at www.catelemd.com

Dedicated to our world's scientists, our
future leaders, and of course,
to my Lennon.

Hi FRIENDS! This is LENNON.

LENNON is just **TWO**.

AND EVEN THOUGH
SHE'S JUST A YOUNG'N
SHE NOTICES LOTS OF
THINGS ARE NEW.

MOM HAS A MASK ON ALL OF THE TIME.

AND DADDY SURE IS HOME A LOT...

WHEN SHE SEES HER
FRIENDS out in the PARK,

SHE WANTS TO **HUG THEM** but cannot.

LENNON HAS LOTS OF QUESTIONS.

WHY CAN'T I see my FRIENDS?

WHY AM I STUCK INSIDE this HOUSE?

WHAT HAPPENED to our WEEKENDS?

well, LENNON –
there's SOMETHING called
CORONAVIRUS.

IT'S A GERM THAT'S
VERY small.

AND IT CAN MAKE SOMEONE VERY SICK –

OLD,

whether they're YOUNG,

OR **TALL.**

SHORT,

it doesn't MATTER WHAT you
LOOK LIKE,
BLACK,
WHITE,
BROWN,
red or blue.

NO MATTER WHAT YOUR COLOR or AGE,

CORONAVIRUS is BOO BOO!

IT GETS INSIDE
THROUGH THE
NOSE or MOUTH

and it can
get out that
way, too!

LIKE WHEN WE
SING OR
YELL OR
COUGH,

OR WHEN
WE GO . . .

BUT IT CAN'T **FLY**
OR JUMP
OR RUN!

SO WE CAN
SHOW WE
CARE

BY KEEPING THE **GERM** FROM HURTING OTHERS

WITH THE **MASKS** WE WEAR.

BUT SOME PEOPLE CAN GET SICKER THAN MOST,

it really isn't fair.

Some **WORK** to make our city **RUN**, THAT'S WHY WE MUST DO OUR **SHARE**!

LENNON GIVES THEM HER APPRECIATION and her *love*

JUST SIMPLE and PURE.

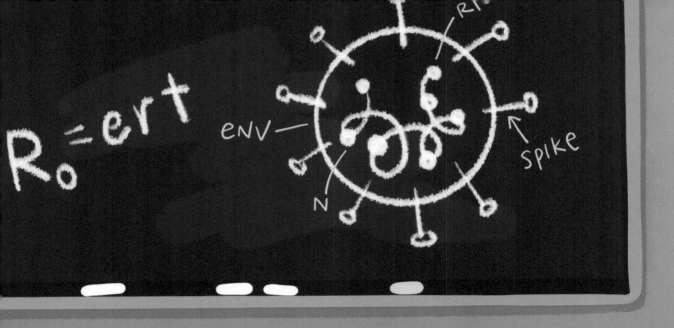

SHE STAYS AT HOME *and*
WEARS A MASK
UNTIL WE CAN FIND A
CURE.

...WHICH will mean getting a SHOT.

OUCH!

LENNON **REALLY** HATES NEEDLES.

BUT IF IT'S HOW WE WILL
BEAT THIS GERM
then she will
DO IT-

FOR
the
PEOPLE!

THOUGH SHE MISSES
HER GRANDMA AND
HER FRIENDS,
and at times,
FEELS SO ALONE,

SHE STILL SEES
THEIR FACES FROM AFAR
and hears them
LAUGH on the TELEPHONE!

SOMETIMES LENNON gets MAD AT CORONAVIRUS.

THAT'S OKAY,
LENNON.

(we get mad, too.)

BUT IF WE STICK
TOGETHER
and DO OUR PART-

THEN i PROMISE
WE WILL MAKE iT THROUGH.

BECAUSE CORONAVIRUS IS JUST ONE OBSTACLE –

remember, IT'S NOT THE END!

IF WE REMEMBER

WHO *and* WHAT

MATTERS MOST,

WE WILL ALL BE TOGETHER SOON AGAIN!

acknowledgements

Thank you to Terrence for his infinite love, enthusiasm, and support, and to Dr. Jennifer Chang for her "infectious" passion for science and the arts.

Here's to believing in our future generations.

ABOUT THE AUTHOR

Dr. Cate Le is an infectious diseases physician based in Los Angeles, California. An immigrant from Vietnam, she was born in a refugee camp in the Philippines and raised in Minnesota. She specializes in general infectious diseases, global medicine, and HIV/AIDS care, and she dedicates her time to fighting against racial and gender inequities in health care. She leads a clinic specializing in care for patients recovering from COVID-19. When she is not practicing medicine, she enjoys creating, writing, raising her daughter, and eating.

CPSIA information can be obtained
at www.ICGtesting.com
Printed in the USA
LVHW071937250521
688479LV00001B/1